STO√

Hail, Nathan Hale!

by MILDRED MILES MAIN

Decorations by
STEPHEN J. VOORHIES

New York • **ABINGDON** • *Nashville*

This book is dedicated to my husband, Charles Oscar Main, whose ancestors lived in Connecticut and took part in the stirring events concerned with the formation of our country.

AUTHOR'S STATEMENT

This fictional biography of Nathan Hale is founded on historical fact insofar as Hale's experiences have been recorded. Parts of his story are not known to anyone. No one knows who betrayed Nathan Hale when he was on his mission for General George Washington. The author of this book has felt justified in using an imaginary character for this villain and has chosen to call him Mark Thorne. The other characters are real.

Appreciation is expressed to Mrs. Frank Cogan, Farmington, Connecticut, who as executive secretary of the Antiquarian & Landmarks Society, Inc., read the manuscript for accuracy.

PREFACE

On a beautiful day, June 6, 1755, Elizabeth Strong Hale looked at her newborn baby boy and smiled. Her husband, Richard Hale, who was a deacon in their church at Coventry in the Colony of Connecticut and often called "Deacon Hale," said proudly, "Elizabeth, now we have five fine sons. Little Elizabeth will have to wait until later for a baby sister. What shall we name this son?"

"Let's name this baby Nathan," said Elizabeth.

So it was decided.

Elizabeth cuddled the baby. "This is another Strong-Hale son!" she said.

Then she and her husband laughed. Elizabeth's maiden name had been Strong, and each child seemed to be "strong" as well as "hale."

After the birth of Nathan, Elizabeth Strong Hale had four more sons and two daughters. One of these sons and a daughter died when young babies so there were ten Hale children left, eight boys and two girls.

No one could think of a happier home. As the years passed Nathan's little brothers, Richard, Billy, and David, played in the fields and gathered eggs in the haymow for their father.

Little Joanna followed her sister, Elizabeth, around the house and played peekaboo behind a long wooden bench, called a settle, that stood near the fireplace in the kitchen.

Enoch and Nathan, being the fifth and the sixth in the sizeable line of children born in the Hale homestead, were in the middle part of the family. They were always together and were bosom "friends" as well as being brothers. They had a close friend named Asher Wright who lived on a neighboring farm.

When Nathan was twelve years old and Enoch a year and eight months older, their mother died.

A great loneliness filled Nathan's heart and he and Enoch "took to their books" and studied hard to try to forget their loss. Their sister Elizabeth, then fifteen years old, and the older brothers, gave strength to Deacon Hale.

Strange and interesting things were going on in the colonies where they lived and Nathan, wise for his years, began to wonder what part he would play in the affairs of the day.

CONTENTS

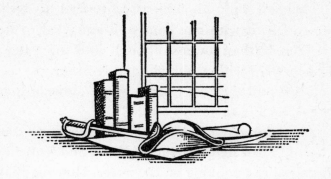

FISHING AND WISHING

"Nathan! Help!" the frantic cry shattered the peaceful, even flowing sound of the Willimantic River, near Coventry, Connecticut.

Settlers were scattered here and there, but none were close to the spot where Nathan and Enoch Hale were in a lone rowboat. The brothers looked in astonishment at Asher Wright, their best friend, who had just tumbled into the water. He had been leaning over to count their fish on the tow line that trailed from their boat. Asher was a good swimmer so the boys were surprised to hear him call for help.

Suddenly, Nathan, who was twelve and the youngest of the three boys, realized what had happened. "Enoch! Asher has a cramp. We must pull him out of the water!"

Nathan flung his fishing rod toward his brother. Enoch caught it with one hand and struggled to steady the boat as Nathan lowered himself into the water and pushed forward with a plunge toward Asher.

"I'll pull the boat over to shore," Enoch shouted, "and get as close to you as I can."

Nathan waved to Enoch to let him know that he had heard. Then he lost sight of Asher. Suddenly he saw his friend's head bobbing on the water. How many times had he gone down?

As he pushed toward Asher, Nathan blamed himself for not taking a larger share of the rowing. Asher must have been too tired.

Nathan said a little prayer as he pushed himself to increase his speed. In a moment, he caught Asher by the short black queue of hair at the back of his head. There was no struggle because Asher had become a dead weight. Nathan entwined one of his arms around his friend and began to swim toward shore. He could not see Enoch following with the boat, and his aching limbs were becoming numb.

But he heard Enoch call, "Good, Nathan, you're almost there. You're the best swimmer in Coventry!"

Nathan knew that more than good swimming would soon be needed. They would have to get the water out of Asher's lungs immediately.

After pushing his friend's limp body on the grass,

Nathan grabbed an overhanging branch of a willow tree and pulled himself ashore. He turned Asher face-downward on the grass and with deft fingers, pushed up under the boy's shoulder blades and then released pressure.

Up and out! Up and out!

As soon as Enoch could tie the boat to the tree, he took over. Using the same movements Nathan had used, he worked. Up and out!

Although Nathan was exhausted from his rapid swim to save Asher, he couldn't rest. "Asher must come out of this!" he kept saying to himself.

Nathan and his brothers and Asher, who lived on a farm near them, were good swimmers. Why they were practically fish! Their homes were almost surrounded by water, and they had been swimming since early childhood.

Lake Wangumbaug, where Mohican Indians had once lived, was two miles northeast of their home. To the west about twenty-five miles away was the big Connecticut River. Just a good walk to the east near the little town of South Coventry was the Willimantic.

Nathan and Enoch took turns working over Asher and, gradually, the color returned to his cheeks.

He smiled wanly at his friends and began to speak slowly. "First time I ever had a cramp. Make light of it, won't you, boys, so as not to frighten my folks?"

"They'll be glad to see you safe and sound," said

Nathan. "They know a cramp can happen to anybody."

All thoughts of the fish and the boat had vanished until Asher told Nathan and Enoch to take it all. "We've had so much fish lately I know my folks won't want any. There's a nice mess for your whole family. Your big sister can cook them for you."

"Suppose you come home with us, Asher, and have supper."

Asher smiled and nodded.

Enoch carried the heavy string of fish, and Nathan steadied Asher as they walked toward the neat frame house belonging to the Hale family. Their farm was a large one, 240 acres. The three boys trudged along over the lush and rolling meadows. "I bet you're going to be great someday, Nathan," said Asher.

"Fiddlesticks," said Nathan, "But I'm glad I caught you in time."

As they approached the house the Hale brothers swarmed out, each asking questions. "You're soaking wet! What happened? Did the boat tip over?" asked Samuel, the oldest.

"Does Mrs. Wright know?" asked John, next to the oldest.

Joseph, the third oldest, ran to get towels. Richard and Billie, the younger brothers, were sent to the Wright house to get permission for Asher to stay for supper.

Deacon Hale had gone to town to talk with the

townspeople about the news in the colony. The boys had been doing the chores. It was about time for their father to return, so Elizabeth who was fifteen, took the situation in hand. Since the death of their mother five months before Elizabeth had been the "mother" of the family.

"Enoch," she said, "you clean the fish. After Nathan and Asher have a chance to get dry and rest a bit they can set the table."

The smell of spicy gingerbread came from the bake-kettle, or Dutch oven, on the hearth, and the fish began to simmer in a three-legged frying pan, called a spider. The odor of cooking hominy and wild celery filled the air. Nathan's nose tingled. "Will we eat soon?"

Elizabeth smiled. "You and Asher can pour the tea, if you are in such a hurry."

The "tea" was a brew of blackberry leaves which many of the colonists had been using since the King, George the Third, had put a tax on tea and several other things that the colonists thought unfair.

As they filled the cups, Asher said, "Maybe the King will change his mind about the tea tax the way he did about his Stamp Act last year."

"Maybe Father will have some news when he gets home from the village," said Nathan. When Deacon Hale came in Nathan and Asher took turns telling about their experience at the river.

Soon supper was called, and Deacon Hale said,

"Asher, since you are our guest tonight we'll seat you above the salt." He motioned to a place between himself and a large salt cellar. They all stood while the Deacon offered the blessing. "Dear Lord," he said, "It is with grateful hearts that we bow our heads. We are thankful Asher has been spared. We are thankful for all the good things thou hast given us. Give us strength to bear our sorrows. Help us to solve the problems we have in our country. May this food nourish our bodies and help us to do our duties in thy name. Amen."

Nathan knew that part of the sorrow his father mentioned was the death of the children's mother. She had died soon after her twelfth child had died as an infant.

Two years passed, and the family was very happy when, in June of 1769, their father married Abigail Adams, a widow from Canterbury.

Nathan and Enoch were studying to enter Yale College although Nathan was only fourteen years old and Enoch fifteen. Both boys were quick, and therefore able to keep up their studies. Their tutor was the Reverend Joseph Huntington, their minister. Nathan and Asher remained good friends, but Nathan's studies were beginning to change their interests.

"It's funny, Nathan," said Asher, one day when

he was over at the Hale home. "You take to books like a duck takes to water, but I think I'll stick to farming. What do you plan to be, Enoch?"

"A minister just like Reverend Huntington."

"And you, Nathan?" questioned Asher.

Nathan pushed back a shock of blond hair and looked at Asher. "I'm not exactly sure. Most of the people around here haven't made up their minds about what to do about the King's demands. Enoch, do you think I should go in for politics? Patrick Henry must be a wonderful speaker. He certainly surprised people in Virginia when he said, 'Caesar had his Brutus, Charles the First his Cromwell, and George the Third—may profit by their example.' "

Enoch spoke up, "We have more to think about than politics right now. What's the past form of this Latin verb?" He shoved a piece of paper toward Nathan, who began to write.

"Let's hurry, and have our Latin lesson finished by the time Mother and Father come home from the church meeting."

Asher looked puzzled. "Nathan, do you call your stepmother 'Mother'?"

"Yes," said Nathan. "She's good to us and keeps us all from being lonely now."

"Besides, she's a big help," Enoch interrupted.

Nathan continued, "Mother told us that when we

get off to Yale in October she will have her two daughters, Sarah and Alice Adams, come to live here. Then there will be lots of girls to help with the housework!"

"Why don't they come now?" asked Asher.

"Father thinks they would keep us from studying, and we might not pass our exams."

"Well, that's what I'm doing now," said Asher. "I'd better get along home. But, I hate to have anything come between us. This learning business is making everything different."

Nathan put down his book. "Asher, sometimes people have to do things they are called upon to do. Father has always wanted Enoch and me to go to college. You know that I'll miss our times together, but maybe we can figure out a way for you to go to New Haven with us for a visit."

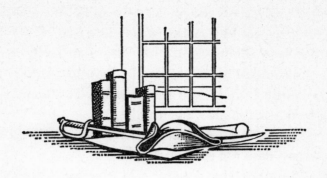

A TEST OF COURAGE

One day in mid-October Asher came over to help the Hale family load hay on wagons so that it could be carried to the barn to be stored. Work was piling up, and the Deacon was anxious to get it out of the way before Enoch and Nathan started off to college.

The school term at Yale ran from the middle of October until the first of September. The Reverend Huntington now felt the boys were well prepared to enter college. For days the boys had been getting their things ready to pack. Mrs. Hale and Elizabeth had already washed everything and packed neat bundles.

The boys had been helping their father every day in the fields so the farm work would be easier for their brothers during the winter months. The chore that needed immediate attention was the haying.

The Deacon raised his pitchfork and suddenly said, "Asher, would you like to ride down to New Haven with the boys? Then you could bring their horses back."

"Would I?" said Asher. "I'd love to go! Besides, I have a cousin living there I could visit. Maybe he could come back with me to Coventry."

"It's sixty miles," said Deacon Hale. "You'll have to take two days for the trip."

"So much the better," said Nathan. "We'll have just that much more time together."

Nathan could see Asher's face cloud as he turned toward the Deacon and said, "I'll be glad to go with the boys, but it will be hard to leave them there."

"I do wish you could go to college with us, Asher," said Nathan. "It's going to be lonesome without you."

"You'll make new friends," said Asher. "But I'll be lonesome here."

The boys were jolted from their thoughts by Deacon Hale. "Hurry up, boys! Pitch more hay onto the wagon!"

The boys began to pitch great forkfuls until it piled high on the wagon and spilled over the edges.

"Wait a minute, boys!" the Deacon shouted. "Don't cover me up!" He stood with a great tuft of hay on the top of his head—looking like a scarecrow.

The boys burst out laughing.

Much to their surprise, the Deacon laughed, too,

and pulled hay out of his hair and shook himself. He said no more about hurrying that day.

For the next few days Nathan's heart pounded with excitement. Finally, it was time to leave for New Haven. Asher came over to go along.

"Here," said Deacon Hale to Enoch and Nathan, "are my three best horses to take. Use them wisely, and I know Asher will bring them back safely."

John and Joseph helped Nathan and Enoch fasten their bags to the saddles. Billy and Richard held the reins. Mrs. Hale, Elizabeth, and Joanna came out to say good-bye and Mrs. Hale put a box of food into Enoch's hands. Then the boys were off for new adventures.

Nathan looked back at his family and his homey dwelling place with his favorite pear tree in the door-yard. He glanced at the meadows, fields, and woods beyond. He would miss this place.

Over the beautiful countryside the boys rode, breathing deeply of the autumn air. As they passed the quiet farms there was little to remind them of the unrest in the country. But Nathan knew that behind the neat hedgerows and stone fences much talk was going on in the farmhouses.

That night they stopped at a comfortable-looking brick farmhouse and asked to stay overnight. As they sat about the supper table they talked with the family, who were happy to have young boys for company.

The conversation soon turned to King George. "What does he think we are?" said the farmer, "He seems to have no interest in us at all except to get our money! Our country is big enough to take care of itself, but the King looks upon us as small children who must be told what to do."

Nathan was interested in what the farmer said, but he was too tired to talk long. Soon, the three boys were asleep in feather beds.

As they rode along the winding trail the next day, Nathan thought about the farmer's remark.

Finally New Haven loomed into view. The boys found themselves in the midst of a sizeable settlement.

"Whew!" said Nathan. "This is the biggest town I've ever seen!"

"Me too," said Asher.

"Look!" said Enoch. "That must be the college."

There stood three important-looking buildings. One was of frame and was painted light blue. Next to it was a big brick chapel building with a huge-faced clock near the top, and above that was a belfry. On the other side of the chapel was a red brick building with cheery green doors. The window frames were pure white.

A tall boy with straight clear-cut features came out of the red brick building and approached the boys.

"Can you tell us where President Daggett's house is?" asked Nathan.

The boy nodded and smiled. "New students, I suppose?"

"Yes," said Enoch. "I'm Enoch Hale, and this is my younger brother, Nathan. Our friend, Asher Wright, came down with us from Coventry. He'll go back home tomorrow."

The boy looked at Enoch and then at Nathan. "Hale Number One and Hale Number Two," he said. "I suppose I ought to call you Hale Primus and Hale Secundus now that you will be in college. You know your Latin, I suppose. My name's Bill Hull—and this is Connecticut Hall where I live."

Then making a sweep of his arm he said, "President Daggett's house is over there."

There stood a big house with cut stone chimneys, and in a nearby field a cow was munching grass.

"Milk with our learning, I see," said Nathan.

They all laughed, and then Nathan noticed Asher's downcast face. He knew what Asher was thinking. Nathan had found a new friend already. What could he do—what could he say to make Asher realize that he would never forget him no matter how many new friends he made? Why they had been friends ever since they were "tadpoles."

Taking him by the shoulders, Nathan said, "Asher, you will have to help keep the folks happy at home. Write us and tell us what you think of our new stepsisters when they come. We'll write you about things here."

Asher's eyes lighted up as he said, "Nathan, I'll never forget that I owe my life to you."

"You may have a chance to save mine sometime," Nathan answered.

"From the hangman's noose, perhaps!" said Bill with a laugh. "I see you have a mole on your neck."

"Well, don't hang me before I even enter," bantered Nathan. "I know you upperclassmen are pretty hard on freshmen."

"Well, I guess we wouldn't go that far," said Bill, and he clapped Nathan on the back and then sauntered toward Connecticut Hall.

Asher tied the horses to a stump and fed them while Nathan and Enoch went to the president's house.

President Daggett met the boys at the door. He wore a long black robe and a white wig. His face was serious but kindly. He ushered the boys into the library.

Nathan noticed the heavily laden bookshelves. "How nice it would be to browse through those books," he thought.

President Daggett looked at a paper on his desk and said, "You will room in Connecticut Hall. Have you met any of the boys?"

"We've met Bill Hull," said Nathan, "and we like him."

"That's good," said the president. "This is Bill's second year at Yale. Sometimes the older boys, especially the juniors and seniors, like to make trouble for the new freshmen. So look out!"

"Yes, we've already heard that," said Enoch.

"Thank you for the advice, sir," said Nathan.

Outside the president's house, the boys joined Asher and together they carried the luggage into Connecticut Hall where Asher said a quick good-bye.

Bill Hull introduced the Hale boys to the students living in Connecticut Hall. One boy was Roger Alden, and he was a descendant of John Alden who had come on the *Mayflower*.

"This is James Hillhouse," said Bill, as a tall boy with a long nose and thin-set lips came forward.

Nathan decided that despite his stern appearance, James would be a lot of fun.

Two older boys, Benjamin Tallmadge and Timothy Dwight, came along to greet Nathan and Enoch. Timothy had graduated in September and although this was the middle of October and the beginning of a new school year, Timothy was still around. He explained that he planned to do a little tutoring.

"Everyone is so friendly," said Nathan. "I've heard that upperclassmen didn't pay any attention to freshmen."

"Well," said Timothy Dwight, "maybe it depends

a little on your attitude. You'll find some upperclassmen who will try to lord it over you, but try to get along with them."

Before long Nathan and Enoch were cozily settled in their room and had met Isaac Gridley—their room-mate.

Isaac reeled off the schedule. "Five-thirty, chapel! Then classes until mid-morning, then time for a short walk, then more classes!"

"Then what?" said Enoch.

"Ah, dinner!" said Isaac, "the most important event of the day. It's our main meal. After dinner we have athletics and then more classes until suppertime."

"Seems like a full day," said Nathan.

Enoch spoke up, "Nathan's good at athletics—and lessons, too."

Nathan said to Isaac, "Like the boys here say, Enoch is 'Hale the First' and he's going to be a minister. You have to be smart *and* good, to be a minister."

The three laughed.

"What are you going to be, Nathan?" asked Isaac.

"I'm not exactly sure," said Nathan. "I'll have to wait until I find a spot where I'll be useful."

A bell sounded and Isaac led the way to the dining room where Nathan and Enoch met the other boys who were to be their classmates.

As the months passed, Nathan, Thomas Mead,

Roger Alden, John Wyllys, and James Hillhouse were together so often the other students called them the quintumviri.

All of the boys liked to read and then discuss their findings after supper. Nathan enjoyed the sessions, and the year passed so quickly that Nathan hardly knew where the time went. With his studies and his interest in athletics, every day was filled.

One evening in March James Hillhouse stopped Nathan in the hall, "Hale the Second, how about you and your older brother coming to my room tonight? One of the fellows was down at Benedict Arnold's store the other day to buy supplies, and he met someone named Mark Thorne. Mark seemed to know so much about the things that are happening in the colonies now, we invited him over to talk with us. He may be a Tory for all I know. If he is, that'll just give us patriots a chance to see how well we debate."

"We'll be there," said Nathan and hurried to tell Enoch.

As they entered James's room that night the place seemed packed. There were boys in chairs, on beds, and on the floor.

When the strange boy across the room came forward to speak, Nathan noticed his peculiar walk. He swayed from side to side. He had a know-it-all smirk that made Nathan immediately dislike him.

As Mark talked glibly Nathan's back stiffened.

Someone asked Mark why King George's soldiers had fired upon the people in State Street in Boston, wounding and even killing some.

"It was their own fault," Mark said. Then he said that he thought the colonists should do what they were told without question.

Nathan could stand it no longer. He rose to his feet. "Mark," he began, "you have a perfect right to your views. You can be loyal to the Crown, if you wish. But I'm not a Tory. You can call me what you like—a rebel—or whatever, but I am for *my* country, America. Our forefathers came here because they believed in freedom. The men of Boston were only trying to protect their rights to have a town meeting. As long as the King let people speak their minds and have a part in law making they were happy. But now the King treats people as if he thinks they are small children."

"And what are you?" scoffed Mark. "A mere child —a freshman! You'd better watch your step, Nathan Hale, or you will get into trouble."

The room was in an uproar.

Bill Hull's booming voice could be heard above the noise.

"Men," he said, "only time will tell who is right, but I agree with Nathan. It takes courage to speak one's mind, and we need men of courage today."

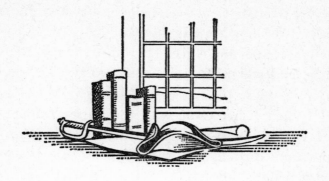

A SECRET TO KEEP

Mark Thorne did not come back to the college, but he lived in New Haven and worked in his father's store, and Nathan saw him sometimes. Nathan could detect his walk anywhere. But Mark always turned away.

Nathan had thought a great deal about the situation in the country and was anxious to get home for vacation to talk with his family. Vacation time came at last. "Now we'll have six long weeks at home," Nathan told Enoch. "It will be fun to see everybody again. Won't Asher love to hear about all the things that we've done!"

Enoch waved a letter that had just come in by post rider.

"Open it, Enoch," said Nathan. "I suppose Father will give us directions and plans for returning."

The letter told them that Asher would bring

horses for them, but something else in the letter especially interested the boys. It was the part that said, "You will get to meet Sarah and Alice. They have come to live with us now, and you will never meet two sweeter, prettier girls."

When Asher came with the horses Nathan and Enoch were ready. It was a beautiful time for a trip. The maples were turning red, and the oaks were beginning to get a little yellow.

"Have you been fishing lately, Asher?" said Nathan. "Any more big black bass to be had? Or is everything quiet in Coventry?"

Asher laughed. "Lots of things have been happening around your house this year," he said. "With the girls there now—whew! All the spinning and cooking!"

"I'd like some good homemade gingerbread and a cup of tea right now," said Enoch.

"You mean blackberry leaf tea, of course," Asher said quickly. "Most of our friends have stopped using tea entirely now."

"That's good," said Enoch.

"That ought to show King George that people don't like taxes that they don't have a voice in making." Nathan picked up a heavy cloth bag and fastened it to his horse's saddle.

As the three boys jogged along they had much to talk about. Asher told how the neighbors in Coventry had helped to build a new barn for Farmer Brown after his burned, about a spelling bee that one of the younger Hale boys had won, and ended with a recount of a quilting party.

"Your brother, John, took Sarah Adams to the party," said Asher. "Everybody says he's sweet on her."

Enoch laughed. Then Nathan said, "That's the only trouble with Yale. There aren't any girls. But we've met some grand fellows—and one not so grand," he added and told Asher about Mark Thorne.

Enoch broke in, "Aren't these horses slower than they were?"

Asher laughed. "That's just because you are anxious to get home."

"To meet the Adams girls," chided Nathan.

"What about you?" said Enoch.

As the boys rounded the bend in the road near the Hale farm Nathan let out a loud "Hello!"

The brothers came running out to meet them. John shouted, "Hello there! Are you so stuffed with knowledge that you are college crabs?"

Little David jumped on the horse behind Nathan and rode with him into the barn lot.

When Nathan saw Alice he could not take his eyes off her. She was a slip of a girl, a year younger than he, but her rounded figure and slender waist made him realize that she was a young lady. Her dark wavy hair was brushed back from her face, and her hazel eyes were dancing. Dressed in a crisp linen dress she had made she was quite a picture, Nathan thought.

Best of all, Nathan loved her laugh, and before he knew it he, too, was laughing for the sheer joy of being home.

Nathan noted that his father looked a little older, that Joanna was bigger, and that Elizabeth seemed more grown-up. She was eighteen now and soon to be married to Samuel Rose, a young man of Coventry.

Nathan smelled the pungent odor of gingerbread.

"Um, it's good to be home!"

"Put your luggage in your room, and then we'll eat," said his mother.

After the boys had washed and were alone in their room, Enoch turned to Nathan.

"My," he said, "Did you ever see a prettier girl than Alice! When I finish college and become a minister I'd like to have a wife like Alice."

Nathan had a lump in his throat. He was happy to be home, but was Alice going to make a difference between him and his brother? He had started to tell Enoch how much he liked her. But he decided to keep the way he felt about Alice to himself.

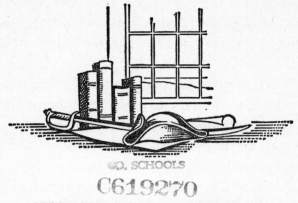

NATHAN FACES A PROBLEM

The weeks of vacation passed quickly. Hunting and fishing with Asher took up some of the time, and then there were chores about the farm to do. Occasionally Nathan and Enoch had long visits with the Reverend Huntington who liked especially to hear about the discussions the boys had at college.

Nathan told his former tutor about the Tory, Mark, who had tried to sway the students.

"The young folks of Coventry are almost all patriots," the older man said. "They will fight for the rights of the Colonies if necessary. Of course, there are some Tories everywhere. They think the King is right—right or wrong. We think he is a man—and most men make mistakes. King George has made several!"

The Reverend Huntington continued, "Some of

the patriots call themselves the 'Sons and Daughters of Liberty.' Most of the women in town have promised not to buy cloth that is made in England but to make their own."

Then Nathan knew why the spinning wheel and weaving loom were in use so much in his house. He often found Alice spinning or weaving and occasionally he visited with her as she worked. But he never said a word to Enoch about his feelings for Alice.

Alice, too, kept her thoughts to herself; however, Nathan had a feeling that she liked him. She made the family happy with her stories about funny little happenings about the farm. Tales about a goat that chased little David and the cow that got out and frightened a neighbor amused Nathan and Asher. But Enoch didn't enter as much into the light conversation.

"He seems to have his mind set on more serious things," said Asher one day. "Have you made up your mind yet—what you're going to be?"

"No," said Nathan, "I haven't quite decided."

No more was said during vacation about future plans, and when Nathan and Enoch were ready to be off for their second year at Yale Asher was there again to go with them and bring back their horses.

In July of their second year at college, Nathan, Enoch, Benjamin Tallmadge, and several others came down with measles. The other boys teased them.

"To think that upperclassmen have the measles!" laughed Bill Hull.

In August, Deacon Hale sent a horse down with a friend. He wanted either Nathan or Enoch to come home for two weeks so that one of them could be measured for new clothes. The two boys were the same size so the same measurements would do for both.

"You go," said Nathan. "I need to practice for the broad-jump contest that is going to be held at the end of the year."

"No, you go," said Enoch. "I got behind in my work while I had the measles. I need to study for my exams. You can practice your jumping at the farm. You won't need to be measured every minute. Anyway, you always were a good athlete.

So Nathan went.

Nathan was with Alice every day. He liked to watch her sew his and Enoch's new clothes. Her graceful arms and dainty hands fascinated him. And Enoch was in New Haven!

One day as Alice was sewing on his coat, she said, "Nathan, you and Enoch are alike in size, but you are so different in other ways."

"What do you mean?" said Nathan. He almost said, "Which do you like better?"

"Oh," said Alice. "There's no difference I can put my finger on—but there is something about you—I can't explain it. I think that you should be a leader of men!"

When Nathan returned to New Haven he thought of Alice's words many times. How could he become a leader of men?

Finally the day of the big outdoor contest came. Despite strong competition Nathan was the leading contender for honors in the broad jump. He had practiced so much that his actions were almost automatic. Farther and farther he jumped. The watchers were in an uproar!

"Hurrah! Hurrah! Nathan has made the biggest broad jump that has ever been made at Yale. He has broken the record!"

Bill Hull patted him on the back and said, "Nathan, you are a good leader!"

Was this what Alice had meant? He wondered. It was all very well to have the boys look up to him because he could run and jump, but how could he make this ability count for something?

"I'd like to be another kind of leader," he thought.

He kept this in mind when he took part in debates and soon he became known as one of the school's best speakers. The Linonia Society considered him one of their leading members.

During his studies and activities, Alice was often on Nathan's mind. He wanted to be what she wished him to be.

In February of his last year at Yale, the bottom fell out of Nathan's world! Alice married Elijah Ripley, a man much older than she. A letter from Asher gave the news.

Nathan wondered if it were possible that Alice could not choose between Enoch and himself and had taken this way out. Maybe she didn't want to face both of them. The idea was unthinkable! Alice had good sense. She should have known that the Hale boys could be good losers as well as good winners. He would much rather have lost Alice to his favorite brother than to anyone else. Who had influenced her?

For a time Nathan was deeply disappointed. He couldn't put Alice out of his mind nor his heart. He threw himself into his studies and finally, graduation day came—September 5, 1773. Thirty-six men dressed in long black gowns lined up to receive diplomas. Nathan stared in admiration at the new watch his family sent him.

Had Alice had a part in choosing this graduation gift? He wondered. It certainly was too bad that Alice could not have come to college with him. She would have been quick to learn. All girls should have a chance to go to college!

These thoughts were racing through his mind when the voice of President Daggett broke through his consciousness. "Nathan Hale, we should like a short speech from you."

Nathan knew that it was often the practice of the president to call upon the graduates to give talks to prove their ability to speak on a moment's notice. He rose to his feet and began in a clear voice, "I shall speak about higher learning for girls. I think women as well as men should have the opportunity of going to college."

Everyone sat up straight. Nathan could almost feel their thoughts. "Girls go to college! Why, they are interested only in sewing and homemaking."

Nathan gave reasons for his thoughts. His audience was attentive. When he sat down there was much applause. After it died down Nathan began to feel that he really should do something to bring about the ideas he had talked about. He would like to teach!

After the graduation ceremony was over, President Daggett said, "Nathan, there is a school at East Haddam, Connecticut, that needs a schoolmaster for next year. Would you like to go?"

"I would like that very much," said Nathan. "Instead of going home this summer I'll visit my Uncle Samuel in New Hampshire. He was a teacher and could give me many good ideas."

So Nathan went East and Enoch returned home before taking a position as a helping minister.

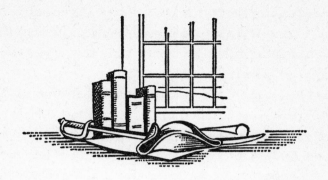

A BEGINNING

Nathan stopped in Boston on his way to his uncle's house in New Hampshire. Boston was teeming with people arguing for liberty from England.

Although he hadn't seen Mark Thorne often in the last three years, Nathan never forgot their first stormy meeting.

"Mark ought to hear some of these people talk," thought Nathan. "I wish he could see the Liberty Pole here."

The Liberty Pole was a tall stick that had been thrust into the ground eight years before at the time of the Stamp Act. It reminded the people of their love of liberty and their dislike for the Stamp Act. Even though King George had ceased asking colonists to buy stamps for their printed materials, he had imposed some other unreasonable taxes. So the people kept the Liberty Pole.

Boston was a most interesting place. Nathan loved the pretty inns with odd names such as "The Goat in Boots" and "The Happy Farmer."

One night when Nathan stopped in one of these inns for supper he listened to the people talk. A big man with a gruff voice sat at the next table with several other white-wigged gentlemen. Suddenly Nathan heard him say, "It's a good thing the tax has been taken off glass and lead and paper. But what about tea? I tell you, if the tax isn't taken off tea, something is going to happen! Mark my words!"

Nathan couldn't help wondering about this, but he had a job ahead of him and he was anxious to get started.

Nathan's conversations with his uncle naturally drifted to the colonists' difficulties with the King.

"Hush," Uncle Samuel said, "it may mean trouble, but don't talk about it when your cousin Samuel comes here tonight. I love him dearly, and I am proud of his standing as a young lawyer here, but I do not agree with his ideas. He is a Tory, so let's not talk about politics when he comes."

At dinner that night Samuel and Nathan talked about college instead of the subject that was most on Nathan's mind. In spite of differences in political views, Nathan and Samuel liked each other.

After a few weeks spent listening to his uncle's advice about teaching, Nathan went to East Haddam, Connecticut. There he started teaching in a little red schoolhouse on the beautiful Connecticut River. From his desk perched high on a platform, Nathan could look down on all his pupils. They were all ages. Some were almost as big as he, and some were very mischievous. Nathan knew that boys and girls need healthy bodies as well as keen minds. He organized games and taught them to play ball. Perhaps that was one of the reasons he had no trouble with the pupils.

In December a letter came to one of the well-known colonial patriots in East Haddam and he shared it with others. Some of the patriots in Boston had banded together to send newsletters to other patriots. These men called themselves "Committees of Correspondence."

Nathan pored over the letter.

Dear Friends and Committee Members:

Several days ago a ship landed in Boston Harbor loaded with tea, and the officials demanded a tax for it. As we had no voice in voting for the tax, we did not want to pay it.

That night, as the boat lay at anchor, fifty men dressed as Indians dumped three-hundred and forty-two chests of tea into the water. That ought to teach King George a lesson. Taxation without representation is tyranny!

Committee of Correspondence

Nathan knew the letter would arouse the people in town. The people of Boston had spunk! Was there a chance for peace? Maybe the King would see his errors and realize that he was dealing with people who would not be bullied. No one was angry with the country of England, but it was folly for the King to think that he could treat his colonists like naughty children. Something would happen. Nathan listened eagerly for news.

Not long after the "Boston Tea Party" the King sent word that Boston Harbor must be closed until the people of Boston paid for the tea they had thrown into the water. British soldiers were sent to carry out this order.

If the port of Boston closed the people would starve. Most of them were fishermen, sailors, or merchants who depended on sailing to other ports to trade goods.

The "crowning insult" to the people of Boston was the King's refusal to let them hold town meetings.

"Now, he won't even let us speak our minds," they complained.

The people of East Haddam sympathized, and Nathan knew that many patriots were fighting mad. What would start the spark?

But he had an exciting job which occupied most of his time. He was making good friends and making good students out of mischievous boys, and he enjoyed every minute of it.

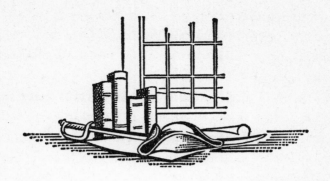

TRUMPET AND DRUM

Nathan had no intention of leaving East Haddam, but the Reverend Huntington had told some of his friends in New London, Connecticut, about Nathan's success as a teacher and a leader in athletics. As a result, he was asked to come to New London the next year to teach older boys. He was only twenty and was to be the master of a new academy! His pupils wouldn't be much younger than he.

"If I can keep them busy learning I don't think I'll have any trouble," thought Nathan. "I'll like New London because it's a thriving coast town."

The harbor of New London had always been busy, but it was especially so at this time since Boston Harbor had been closed.

Nathan rented a room at the home of a pleasant

couple whose niece, Betsy Adams, was living with them. Betsy reminded Nathan of Alice Adams, and he said, "It seems as if I'm always meeting someone nice named Adams!"

Betsy smiled. "Adams is an important name in our colonies today. Samuel Adams is loved by every loyal colonist. He is a wonderful leader!"

"Good," said Nathan. "Then *you* are a patriot if you talk like that!"

He told his new friends about his family and about Sarah and Alice. But he didn't tell them how he had felt about Alice.

Enoch was living in a nearby town doing further preparation for the ministry. Nathan received letters from him often but he didn't say much about his trips home. Then, in December, Enoch wrote that Elijah Ripley had died and Alice was a widow!

Nathan was so busy with his new work, however, that he did not have time to think of much else. Remembering the talk he had given at Yale on his graduation day about the need for girls to have as good an education as boys, he decided to do something about it.

He went to the board which had charge of his school and told them he would like to start a class for girls, since they should have access to more education than they had been given.

"The boys come at seven o'clock in the morning

and I'm busy with them all day, but I'm willing to come at five o'clock in the morning," said Nathan. "If the girls are interested in more schooling they will come at that time."

Twenty girls in their teens came to the school. They wanted to learn other languages as well as their own; they wanted to know something about science; and they wanted to read fine books.

Nathan had learned a great deal about the literary works of his day and the old classics while gathering books together for a library for his club at Yale. The Linonia Library had become known to some of the people in New London, and they asked Nathan's advice when choosing books for their library.

Many important people of town came to see "Master Hale" about one thing and another. One young man, Gilbert Saltonstall, often talked with him, and they became good friends. Nathan called him "Gil Salt" for short.

Gil was a Harvard graduate. He was quiet, thoughtful, a little older than Nathan, but they had many things in common. Like Nathan, he was a loyal patriot.

Nathan made two other good friends in New London—Stephen Hempstead and Tom Fosdick. Steve was tall and sandy-haired and knew "all there was to know about boats," Nathan thought. Tom was a bright-eyed young man a little younger than Nathan.

The four—Nathan, Gil, Steve, and Tom—often went out on Steve's sailboat in the evenings. It made Nathan remember fishing and boating with Asher Wright at home. He wondered how Asher was.

Nathan liked New London. Its salty air and interesting harbor smells appealed to him. The smell of ginger and coffee, molasses and bananas, made him think of faraway places—and adventure. The fishing smacks came in loaded with cargo. The merchant sloops looked pretty with their sails fastened to the one tall mast in the center of the deck.

One night, as the four friends were pulling into shore after a sail, they noticed a strange boat in the harbor.

"It's a British merchant sloop!" said Gil.

"That's odd," said Steve. "Most of the British merchant boats land at New York now. There are a number of Dutch people there, and many of them are Tories who trade with the English. Now that Boston Harbor is closed most of the people in New London have stopped trading with British firms."

"Let's not land until we are sure what they are going to do," said Nathan.

Steve threw out the anchor a short distance from shore. The four kept busy straightening out the ropes and sails, but they watched the British ship every minute.

Soon they saw a man coming down the hill toward the harbor. He was tall and slender, and he swayed from side to side as he walked. He was carrying a package. Nearer and nearer came the man and walked up the gangplank of the British ship.

Nathan whispered to Steve. "It's Mark Thorne! I knew him in New Haven. He was working in his father's store there. I wonder what he's doing here. His father must have some deal with the British, and Mark is carrying it out!"

Steve said, "Maybe he's joining the British merchant ship as a member of its crew. Or maybe he's been here to see whether the people in New London are friendly to the British or not. Anyway, let's see what happens."

Soon the British ship pulled anchor and set sail in the direction of New York.

"Well," said Tom when the boat had pulled out. "I was thinking the four of us might have to take on that bunch of Englishmen in a battle."

Gil laughed. "We're not in war yet."

"Do you really think it might come to war, Gil?" said Tom. "It might." Gil looked thoughtful. "What do you think, Nathan?"

Nathan said, "Well, if it does come I hope I can help my country in some real way."

"I'll help you—whatever you do, Nathan!" said Steve.

"I know I can count on that!" said Nathan.

"I'm with you too, Nathan," said Tom.

There was a sound of pounding hooves on the post road. "What is that?" said Tom. "It's 'way past time for a post rider."

"Hear ye! Hear ye!" called a voice. "Meet at Miner's Tavern!"

"A town meeting!" said Nathan. "Let's hurry! There may be trouble."

People hurried out of their houses and followed the rider to the tavern. A man stood on the doorstep beating a drum. Another blew a trumpet.

The people crowded into the room, and those who couldn't get in stood outside and looked through the door.

Finally, the drum and trumpet were quiet.

A man jumped on a table and shouted, "Men and women of New London—the British have struck at Lexington and Concord. They have killed some of our loyal colonists. It means war! What are you going to do?"

Then Nathan jumped to the table. His long-tailed wool waistcoat and tight-fitting breeches made him look especially tall. His silver buckles shone in the candlelight.

"The schoolmaster!" people shouted.

"I say," began Nathan in a loud ringing voice, "let's take up arms until we have our independence!"

The room buzzed with excitement.

"I'm joining the Continental Army!" said Steve.

"I am too!" said Tom as one man began taking names of those who promised to join the Continental Army.

"I'm going to ask for service near home because my father is very ill and I cannot leave him now," Gil said. "And you, Nathan—you can't go until school is closed! You have given your promise to the board. The students are counting on you to stay too."

Gilbert paused for a moment. "Why Nathan, you should be an officer. Ask for a commission. It will take a little time for that to be granted and maybe school will be over by the time it comes."

Nathan wanted to throw himself into the fight for independence as soon as he could. Yet, Gil was right. He had given a promise. He must finish his work with the new class of girls as well as his class of boys. He wanted them all to pass examinations.

As he walked to the house where he roomed the sound of the trumpet and the drum rang in his ears.

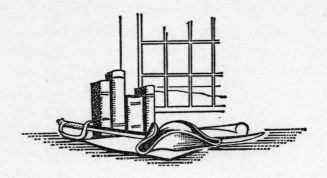

DANGER ALONG THE COAST

That night Nathan tossed and tumbled in his bed. His mind was too filled for him to sleep soundly. The stirring taps of drums, blares of trumpets, and the speeches and shouts of people echoed in his ears. But he had made a promise to teach this year! Gilbert Saltonstall had reminded him of that. He must stick by his promise.

Burning with a desire to help in the struggle for independence, Nathan wrote to the General Assembly of the Colony of Connecticut and asked for a commission.

Meantime, he worked hard. Sometimes he sat grading papers far into the night. The warm glare of the candles helped to keep him awake. Then up at dawn! There was never a minute to waste.

In May, 1775, word came to New London that the

Continental Congress had met for the second time in Philadelphia. They had met first in April right after the trouble at Concord. At the second meeting they appointed George Washington as Commander in Chief of the Continental Army. Nathan was very happy, because he knew what a fine man George Washington was.

In July, Nathan's commission arrived. He was appointed a First Lieutenant of Company Three under Major Latimer in Colonel Webb's Seventh Regiment. Nathan's old friend, Bill Hull, was given a commission as First Lieutenant of Company Two in the same regiment. Nathan was delighted. There was some chance that he would see Bill when they got into action!

Nathan was ordered to go about the towns along the coast of Connecticut and enlist more soldiers. It was two weeks before the end of the school term, but Nathan felt that his students were advanced enough with their work that he could leave them.

He appeared before the board, and looking earnestly at the men seated about the long table, he said, "Sirs, the time has come when I must go. My classes are now fully prepared so that I feel that I can leave them. I am asking to be released so that I may give my services to my country."

"Go with our blessing!" said one of the board members. "And may you help us gain our independence!"

It was hard for Nathan to leave the students he

had learned to know so well. One of the older boys said, "Master Hale, I wish I could be your drummer boy in the army."

"You keep the love of independence beating in your heart like a drum!" Nathan said. "Later, your help may be needed."

Nathan mounted his horse and was off to get more recruits for the colonial army.

In the town squares he talked with crowds who gathered to hear his words. Men in homespun breeches left their farms and fields and stores to follow him. They drilled in the pastures and fields of the farms.

Women gathered their pewter plates and mugs and melted them for bullets. Patriots from the countryside brought all kinds of guns for the men.

Nathan didn't have time to go back to Coventry to see his family, but he heard from his father that they were saving their wool, and the women of the family were weaving blankets and knitting wool stockings for the army for the coming winter.

Nathan was happy that his family was thoughtful. He could almost see Alice weaving by the high front window.

"I tell you, Gil," he said one day when he was recruiting soldiers in New London, "the women patriots are soldiers too! No wonder General Washington feels better. The men stood up well under fire at Bunker

Hill in June, and since that time the fighting spirit among all the people has grown. I can hardly wait to be in the thick of the fight!"

Finally word came to Major Latimer that British ships were nearing Stonington, an important port town just twelve miles east of New London on the coast of Connecticut along Long Island Sound.

Major Latimer ordered Nathan to join him and take his New London company to Stonington. Nathan was then head of ninety men and had the duties of a Captain although his rank and pay were still that of Lieutenant.

"Men," he said in a ringing voice that gave courage, "we are ordered to go to Stonington to chase off English boats near the coast there. They seem to be planning to land and we must stop them."

He went on, "Those of you who have horses, take them. Those who do not, go by foot. We will meet at the shore near the docks at Stonington!"

No one hesitated. Those ships must not land!

Leading his men, Nathan pushed his way down the path along the coast. In spots it was narrow and steep. At other places, underbrush slowed the pace. It grew darker and darker, and began to rain. Thunder rolled like kettledrums and streaks of zigzag light flashed across the sky. Still the men marched forward. They were determined that the English boats should not land.

Finally through the mist they saw the docks of Stonington. When the lightning flashed, they could see two small British boats about to land. A third boat was near the shore.

"Forward, men!" shouted Nathan. "We must stop them now if we can! If they land we will have to fight hand to hand!"

The men shouldered their weapons and crept toward the docks. British soldiers were getting off two of the ships. The third one was still in the water, off shore.

Nathan and his men rushed forward, and the fight was on! The British soldiers were surrounded, and could not move without being shot.

"Keep them covered!" shouted Nathan. "The sailors can't fire the ship's guns without shooting their own men."

The British soldiers were bewildered. Their boats were beginning to move away to avoid capture.

Some of the men jumped into the water and swam with all their might toward their boats. The ones on the shore were taken prisoners.

"Good work, Lieutenant Hale!" said Major Latimer.

The people of Stonington swarmed to the place where the skirmish had taken place. The rain did not dampen their spirits. "Down with tyranny! We want our independence!"

The next morning Nathan and other officers had breakfast with Andrew Main, a patriot of Stonington. Many of the men of his family enlisted in the Continental Army.

Other families also enlisted in great numbers. The spirit of independence was growing.

Shortly after this, Nathan and some of his men were given orders to go on duty in the sloop "Dauntless" with Captain Pond. They were to cruise along the coast and look for other British ships that might try to land. But the British boats had gone elsewhere so the men returned for further orders.

Nathan could not help thinking of Mark Thorne and what he might be doing at this time.

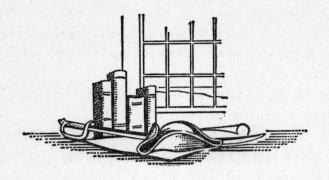

WINTER HILL

In September, 1775, Nathan received orders to march with his men to the Winter Hill encampment near Boston. They started with high spirits. Each night Nathan wrote in his diary. By September twenty-fourth they were marching to music through Providence, Rhode Island.

> Yankee Doodle went to town
> Riding on a pony;
> He stuck a feather in his cap
> And called it macaroni!

The men sang while the fifes and drums played.

They reached Winter Hill on the evening of September 29.

"What a good name for the camp!" said one of the men. "The white canvas tents look like snow on the hillside!"

In all directions, spreading from the top to the bottom of the hill, were thousands of white tents made from the sails of ships and huts made of boards and stone or sticks and mud.

Here and there men heated their soup or stew in big iron kettles over wood fires.

It was a warm evening so Nathan and some of his men stretched out on the ground to rest. They did not know what might happen before morning. The British were encamped in Boston, near enough that their cannons could do damage to the encampment of the colonials on Winter Hill.

The colonial troops hoped to keep the British bottled up in Boston or to drive them away entirely. The Colonials didn't want to start trouble, but they would watch and wait.

It was Nathan's job now to make good soldiers of men who were new at the business of being soldiers. Some of them, away from home for the first time, were unhappy.

Nathan knew that the best way to cure unhappiness was to keep busy so that there would be no time to feel sad or discouraged. He drilled his men and kept them occupied with races and games.

Feeling that it would help morale as well as make them look better, Nathan had his men dress alike. These were the first uniforms the common soldiers had. They were fringed linen shirts belted at the waist and fitted leggings with buckles just above the shoe tops. Soon many of the other companies began to wear this uniform too.

When the weather became colder the blankets and wool stockings sent by Nathan's family in Coventry came in handy. As he curled up under one of the blankets he wondered if Alice had made it, and he wondered when the trouble with England would be over and if Enoch and Alice were seeing each other while he was away.

"It doesn't matter," he thought. "My job is to defend my country from the tyranny of the King. When we have gained independence it will be time enough for me to think of a home of my own."

Nathan knew that many of the colonists had no plan of asking for independence from England at that time. They simply wanted to get the British soldiers out of the country so they could continue with town meetings and govern themselves under their colonial governors. But Nathan also knew that the desire for America's independence from England was growing.

In December Nathan was made a captain. At the same time Bill Hull was made captain of another company on Winter Hill. They often visited in their tents when they were not on duty.

One night, after their men had gone to bed, the two friends sat talking in Bill's tent. The moon cast a shadow over the tents which were white with snow.

"I don't see how our poorly trained men can stand up against the British," said Bill. "We haven't enough guns."

"We must—and we can," said Nathan quickly.

Bill went on talking, "The weather is cold, and the days are dark much of the time. The men are restless and unhappy. Some who enlisted for a short term are leaving. Some have even left for home before their terms were up."

"Yes, I know," said Nathan. "We must think of ways of keeping them."

That night Nathan lay awake planning something to make his men feel better and be better soldiers.

He called them together around the campfire. "I'm proud of every man in this company," he said. "You have been doing well in your exercises, and with our new uniforms the British will know that we are an army working together. We must always keep in mind that *we are all for one and one for all.*

"I'm going to give you points for improvement in drills and for care of your uniforms. Try to make the best record you can for yourselves and I will try to work out vacation time for the most deserving men."

The men began to stand straight. They took sidelong glances at their uniforms as though they realized for the first time that they were badges of honor.

As they filed away to their huts Nathan was glad

that their faces showed pride and determination, but he realized the men's morale would slump again if they became too cold and hungry. What could he do to keep his men well fed and cheerful?

On December 7, Nathan received a letter from Tom Fosdick asking to be transferred to his company. Tom had been in Gilbert Saltonstall's company, but now, with Gilbert's consent, he wanted to join Nathan's group.

The transfer was made.

"Tom, I can't tell you how happy I am to see you," said Nathan. "I have a great group of men—but we need someone like you to keep up our courage. Remember the time we saw the British sloop in the harbor at New London? We didn't have to fight Mark Thorne and his friends that night, but we don't know what is ahead of us now!"

Tom's eyes shone. "I'm at your command, Captain Hale."

By the middle of December the men were grumbling about how long it took the pay to come in. Nathan's pay was slow in coming, too, but he did not have time to think about this. He was only thinking how he might get money for his men.

As he was sitting in his tent after drilling all day a tall, sandy-haired soldier opened the tent flaps.

Nathan looked up. "Steve, old boy! Steve Hempstead!" he said. "How did you get here?"

Steve tossed a bundle into the middle of the tent floor.

"I'm enlisting in Captain Hale's company! Here are my things. I served in the Battle of Bunker Hill, but when that term of service was up I enlisted again, this time in your company."

"Good old Steve! Now we will see a change for good. With your help and Tom's we can do much. If we had a boat we could have a good fishing trip like the ones we used to have together in New London—but we have a job to do now making good soldiers out of our men! Our cause of freedom must not be lost!"

That night, after Steve had gone off to bed and the other men were asleep, Nathan sat thinking. An idea came to him, "I will make a set of rules for my men to follow and they will be more sure of themselves. I will make a copy for each man in my company. They will set an example for other soldiers on Winter Hill."

Then Nathan made up his mind that his men would have better arms and pay even if he had to use his own money to pay them. Before Christmas he borrowed money on the salary that he would get later.

Calling his men together he spoke, "I know that you are brave and deserve warm quarters and better pay. But that cannot be. Your chief payment must come from joy of service to your country. I have arranged, however, to grant home leaves for men who will serve another

63

term." He hesitated. "And I have arranged to give you your pay that is overdue now."

He did not tell them that the money was coming from his own pocket.

"Captain Hale!" the men shouted. "Hail! Captain Hale!"

General Washington wanted to change the positions of his men in the army, and decided this would be a good time. Nathan was sent home to Coventry to recruit more soldiers.

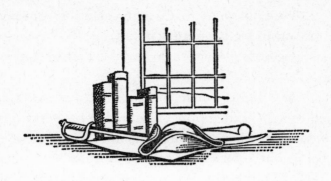

A DIFFICULT DECISION

It seemed strange to Nathan to be on his way to Coventry. He had been in the Continental Army five months now, and so far it did not seem to be gaining much headway. The goal was different for different people. Some people were afraid to take a stand for independence. Almost all the colonials wanted to get the British troops out of Boston, but if they succeeded—then what?

There were many people who felt that if the colonials stopped with that as their goal, the same trouble with the English rulers would happen all over again. Nathan felt this way too. The colonies must be free once and for all. He and the other patriots had no dislike for their mother country, England, yet they felt that the colonies were able to govern themselves without help.

Before he went to Coventry Nathan stopped in New Haven to see his old friends. James Hillhouse, now a promising young lawyer, invited Nathan to stay at his home.

That night, when they were seated at a table lighted by a flickering, pungent smelling bayberry candle, James said, "Nathan, do you remember the talks we used to have in our rooms after supper at Yale?"

"I certainly do. We thought we had the answers to all the problems, then, didn't we?"

"Wonder what happened to that Mark Thorne who was so disagreeable," said James.

Nathan told about seeing Mark board a British boat in the New London Harbor.

"And you've heard nothing more about him?" said James.

"Not a word. Neither have Tom and Steve, who are both in my company. Gil writes to me often from New London and sometimes even sends me the newspaper published there. He hasn't said a word about Mark either. I think Mark must have gone into military service for the British." Nathan put his hand down on the table with a thud. "We've got to beat them, James!"

"How are things at Winter Hill?" asked James.

"Fairly quiet. We're trying to make good soldiers out of untrained men and to keep the British from coming inland at other points. It is bad enough to have them in Boston! General Washington is planning something new, and I am off to get recruits."

"Now is the time for men to become great by gaining independence for our country. I shall do everything I can to help the patriots!"

"Good for you, James! I knew I could count on you!"

Nathan slept soundly that night, secure in the thought that matters were going to improve.

With the help of James Hillhouse, Nathan was able to recruit a number of soldiers in New Haven and in nearby villages. His spirits were soaring when he reached Coventry.

His family crowded around to greet him. His father was older but still straight and tall.

Then he looked at Alice. She was more beautiful now, at nineteen, than he had ever seen her.

Alice showed Nathan the stockings she was knitting and the new blanket that she and their mother had just finished and Nathan said, "You women help more than you will ever know. With God's help and your help, we *will* win independence."

"Samuel feels exactly the same way," said his sister, Elizabeth, who was just coming in.

Elizabeth had married Samuel Rose two years before, and they now had a home in Coventry.

Mrs. Hale spoke up, "Nathan, Enoch wrote us

that you were coming. He couldn't get away from his work for a while, but he will be here before you go back, anyway."

"And John?" said Nathan. "Will I get to see John and Sarah?"

"That you will," said Alice, "They're as happy as two turtledoves."

A happy thought flashed through Nathan's mind. Wouldn't it be nice if the trouble with England were settled and he could marry Alice—that is, if she would have him.

Another thought occurred to him. What about Enoch? Did he still love Alice?

He asked Alice if she ever heard from Enoch.

"Oh, he's fine," she said, "enjoying his work as a minister."

"Does he come over often?" Nathan wondered if her cheeks would color.

"Not often," she said calmly. "He's too busy—but he writes. Enoch is such a serious person. Sometimes I think that he feels that I'm too lighthearted. I like to talk about the serious things of life sometimes. With you —I feel more at ease."

"Alice," said Nathan, "it seems a long time since I've had a chance to talk and laugh with you or with anybody. This war business takes all the laughter out of a person."

"Suppose we forget it while you are here and laugh the way we used to."

Nathan decided that when Enoch came he could see how things were between him and Alice.

The following day, Nathan recruited in the village of Coventry and other small towns. Among those who signed up was his old friend Asher Wright.

"I'll go along with you," said Asher. "After all, you saved my life, and I'm not about to forget that."

"What a team I will have—you, Tom, and Steve! We can lick the enemy alone!" Nathan laughed.

It felt good to laugh, and he and Asher and Alice planned good times for the holiday.

The days slipped by quickly. Then Enoch arrived —his favorite brother!

"You look wonderful, old boy," said Enoch.

"I guess camp life agrees with me," said Nathan. "We don't have fancy food, but so far we have managed. I get hungry sometimes for Mother's ginger cookies and those delicious apple dumplings Alice makes."

"Speaking of Alice," said Enoch, "hasn't she become a beauty? Now that I'm becoming settled in my work I hope to interest her in becoming my wife."

Nathan swallowed hard.

Then he spoke slowly, "Well, you're lucky if you can win her. As for myself, I must help win independence for our colonies before I think of settling down."

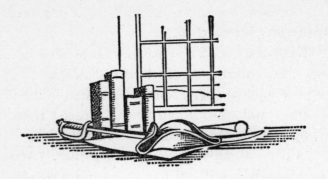

WHERE WILL THEY STRIKE

By the time Nathan reached Winter Hill with his fresh recruits he found that General Washington had the new plans ready.

Nathan and his company had orders to leave Winter Hill and go to Roxbury, which was southwest of Boston and nearer the British Army.

"Now we will get action!" said Nathan to Asher. "The British are still bottled up in the city but if we get all around them—I wonder what they will do then! Something more is bound to happen!"

The chill winds which blew over the hills did not cause the men to complain. They were beginning to feel strength in their cause. The Whigs, the colonists who wanted to separate from England, were gaining in numbers.

About this time, Thomas Paine, a Whig, wrote a small book called *Common Sense* that made people think more about separation.

Nathan went to the towns near Roxbury to buy supplies for himself and for his company. As he bought some big warm barcelona kerchiefs, he listened to the men talking in the stores. Talk of independence was everywhere.

Nathan heard a man speak up fearlessly, "Thomas Paine has done wonders! He has made a number of Tories into Whigs! His facts are true, his thoughts clear!"

"You're right!" said another man. "He's made a Whig out of me! A short time ago I wouldn't have thought of our country separating from England, but now I don't see any other way!"

Nathan broke into the conversation. "Keep up the spirit and we will win! The spirit of 1776 will be known forever! Would any of you like to join in the fight for independence?"

"I would! I would!" shouted some of the men.

The ranks of the Continental Army grew.

In March Nathan moved his men and cannon to the hills right above Boston where the British Army was still encamped. They were to take along food enough for three days, and they were to get there without the British seeing them.

Many other companies, among them Bill Hull's,

were ordered to go too. In all there would be two thousand men on the move! How could they get there without the British knowing it?

The officers thought of a plan, and Nathan hurried to carry out his part. He called Steve, Tom, and several others. "Get some carts of hay and bring them here. We will need them tonight." He told some men in his company to fill other carts with sand.

That night the moon was full and bright, and the carts were ready. Some of the soldiers planned to hide themselves and the cannon under the hay. Wagons filled with sand would trundle along beside them. They hoped the British soldiers would mistake them for merchants as they passed the British guards.

Nathan's heart beat fast. They must get through! He made a last-minute check to see that everything was in order. Then the carts started off one or two at a time.

Rumble! Creak! The carts rolled over the rough streets.

Finally all the carts got through, and by the light of the moon Nathan and his men made a fence of sand and hay on top of the hill. They could hide behind it if the British fired upon them!

Hours ticked away. Nathan looked at his watch anxiously. It was almost daybreak. The cannon were in position.

They watched and waited.

"Do you think the British will try to blow us off the hill, Captain?" said one of Nathan's men.

"They may, or they may just get out of Boston if they feel we are too strong for them. We must watch every minute!"

The hours passed slowly, but the men were alert. Every twig that made a crackling noise might mean a surprise attack.

A drenching March rain and strong wind made the men miserable. Yet they watched and waited all the same. Rain might give the British a chance to attack more easily.

Finally, a guard shouted, "The British are leaving Boston! The boats are ready, and the men are going toward them!"

"It's too good to be true," thought Nathan.

A column of red-coated men could be seen going toward the docks. As soon as the British soldiers were entirely cleared out of Boston, a great shout went up.

"We certainly surprised them by taking this hill!" someone called.

"The Red Coats have gone to Halifax!" shouted another.

Halifax belonged to England so the British soldiers would be safe there, plotting their next move.

Nathan knew that General Howe would strike some other place. *Where?*

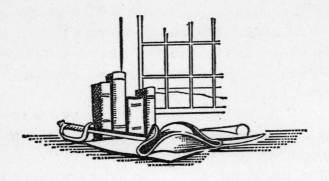

A THRILLING ADVENTURE

Major Latimer summoned Nathan and several other captains to his headquarters one evening. "General Washington feels that Howe and his men will strike New York next. It's an important harbor, and the city is full of Tories."

The major leaned over the map which lay in front of him on a table. His lips were tightly drawn and his face showed tension. "Look," he said, "this is how we must defend New York. We must make a fence, or breastworks, facing the shore of Long Island. This island is at the mouth of the Hudson and East rivers which surround the main part of the city on Manhattan Island. If we guard the harbor from Long Island we can keep the British from landing there.

"Captain Hale, you will take your company to

Long Island at once to help construct the breastworks."

Nathan's men moved by foot and then by ferry-boat to the island and started work. For three weeks they labored to make the breastworks as strong as possible—a defense line of twenty miles.

"Now," said Nathan. "We are ready. In case of an attack by the enemy, we can hide behind the breastworks and level our cannon at them."

While Nathan and his men were working on Long Island, others built Forts Lee and Washington on opposite sides of the Hudson River. Brooklyn Heights was fortified and General Putnam, with half the army, occupied this spot.

No one knew where or when the British would strike. They must continue to watch and wait.

While the colonials were waiting, Nathan and his men went about the city when they were not on duty. Manhattan was a short ferryboat ride from Long Island. Nathan loved the pretty parks and walks along the shore of the Hudson and East rivers. Sometimes he took his men down to Battery Park for training.

One day Nathan and Asher went into a fisher-man's hut near the wharf to buy fish while his men went to a greengrocer's stall.

Suddenly a wild noise filled the air.

Down the street, his men were riding a man on a rail. The man was yelling, "Let me off, you Rebels!"

Nathan saw that the man was Mark Thorne.
"Let him down at once!" shouted Nathan.

"He's a Tory!" shouted the men.

"I know," said Nathan, "but riding the enemy on a rail isn't within the rules of war. Let him down!"

If Mark recognized Nathan he did not reveal it. Instead, he mumbled, "You Whigs are a bunch of bullies!"

He strode off, swaying from side to side, toward the dock where a rowboat waited to take him to a merchant sloop anchored in the harbor.

What did Mark's presence in New York mean? Was he buying supplies for the British? Nathan wondered. He would report the incident to his Major.

During the summer, General Howe and his army appeared in the harbor with a fleet of boats. The thirty thousand British soldiers encamped on Staten Island near Long Island.

What could Washington's army of eighteen thousand men do?

Day by day it became more difficult to get supplies for the colonials with British boats around. Nathan spied the British man-of-war *Asia* at anchor near the harbor with a sloop alongside loaded with food for the British army.

"I tell you, Asher, it isn't fair for the British troops to have all those supplies that were taken from our farms and villages! Our army needs them badly! Men can't fight with empty stomachs!"

"Well, then let's get that supply ship," said Asher. "You know that Tom and Steve and I are willing to help you."

Nathan was thoughtful. "Asher you are good with a rowboat. Rent one as if you were going fishing. Row to the point where the big willow tree stands. It's not far from there to where the *Asia* is anchored. Keep near the shore, out of sight, and pull into a little cove and wait for me. Steve and Tom and I will come when it begins to turn dark. Be careful!"

Nathan, Tom, and Steve waited until about dark. Nathan threw his black barcelona kerchief about his neck. "This may be useful," he said. "Steve, you take Asher's kerchief."

Tom shoved a sharp knife into his pocket.

The three picked their way to the big willow tree on shore. Scarcely breathing they took their places in the boat.

Time passed slowly. Nathan had ordered complete silence.

The four men sitting silently in the rowboat could clearly hear the men talking on the British boat.

"All's well!" came the words of the night watch.

Still Nathan did not give the signal to Asher to start rowing.

Again and again the night watch called out, "All's welll"

Then, at the darkest point of the night, just before dawn, Nathan gave the signal.

Asher dipped the oars into the water so carefully hardly a ripple was made.

Up and out of the water went the oars. As the boat reached the side of the sloop, the men made sure that the rowboat did not jar it.

Nathan grabbed the anchor chains and climbed up hand over hand. Steve and Tom were close behind.

Looking over the side of the sloop, Nathan saw the guard standing with his back toward him. Beyond the guard were the open hatches. Below the hatches were the deck hands, sound asleep. If he could only reach the guard!

Quietly Nathan climbed over the side of the sloop, and before a sound could be made, his black kerchief was tied around the guard's mouth. Steve tied the guard's hands behind him with the other kerchief, while Tom closed the hatches.

Not a sound must be made! The cannon on the *Asia* were just above them!

Tom cut the rope that bound the sloop to the warship and they set sail for the city docks. Steve was an experienced skipper, and there was not a jar to alarm the sleeping men below deck.

When the sloop arrived with the food stuff for the colonial army, a great shout arose.

"This food may save us!" said Nathan's Major. "It will cheer the men greatly! General Washington shall hear of this."

"I would like to do even more for my country, Sir," said Nathan.

OUTWITTED

For weeks nothing seemed to be happening as far as the war was concerned. The colonists watched and waited on Long Island while the British watched and waited on Staten Island. Other things were going on inside the colonies, however.

On June 3, Nathan wrote Enoch from New York. "General Washington is at the Congress, being sent thither to advise on matters of consequence."

The matter of consequence was the signing of the Declaration of Independence in Philadelphia on July 4, 1776.

Nathan's men shouted when they heard the news. "At last Congress has declared what has been in our minds and in our hearts!"

Months passed before the British made a move.

The colonials were trying to make their positions safe and enlarge their numbers. They chopped down trees, dug trenches, and built fences of earth along the New York river banks.

During rest periods Nathan wrote to his family and friends. He hardly dared to think of Alice. He knew Enoch was doing well in his work, but whether he was winning Alice's heart he did not know.

General Washington left many men on the southern side of Long Island and took Colonel Webb's regiment, including Nathan's company, to Brooklyn Heights, which was on the northwestern side of Long Island, nearest New York City. They would be ready wherever the attack broke. It was a game of cat and mouse!

In late August, the blow fell. The British Army landed on the southwest shore of Long Island and advanced in three divisions. Two attacked the defenses in front and one in the rear. The breastworks which had been so carefully made during the summer proved to be little protection.

Nathan, stationed on Brooklyn Heights, was disturbed. He realized no one knew where the British would strike next. Cannon booms filled the air. Scouts brought news. It was going badly for the Continental Army! The British outnumbered them four or five times so the battle was short and onesided. Of the four thousand colonials fighting, one thousand were killed or wounded. Others were captured.

The remaining men retreated to the entrenchments on Brooklyn Heights where Nathan and his men awaited orders.

Would Washington command them to make a counterattack? Or were the British too strong in numbers for all the colonials together?

Nathan knew that sometimes it was necessary to lose battles in order to win a war. He was confident that if General Washington felt the battle would be lost even with added troops, he would try to save the main part of his army.

Everyone was discouraged. A steady rain fell. The men were wet, hungry, and muddy.

Nathan tried to comfort them even though he himself was weak and aching.

"You ought to go to bed, Captain," said Asher. "You look sick."

"I don't feel well," said Nathan, "but the men mustn't know it. My heart is sick at the loss of our men, and I can't do anything about it. Asher, I would do *anything* to help our cause. We must not lose!"

Nathan could not be persuaded to go to bed. He worked both day and night comforting the men.

Orders came from General Washington to obtain boats of all sizes and shapes.

The men wondered how they could ever get off the island without being seen by the British. Scouts brought word that the British were planning to cut them off from New York City. Excitement was high.

The next night a fog formed over the island. The British had stopped their fire for the night, assuming they had the colonial troops in a trap, but General Washington had planned an escape route.

The troops must get to shore without being seen. There were British scouts everywhere. The wounded were carried to waiting boats. Men and horses worked to get guns and ammunition on board.

"How can we expect to get ten thousand men across the river without being discovered!" said one discouraged soldier. "The river's almost a mile wide here!"

"Never mind," said Nathan. "If General Washington thinks we can do it—we will."

The will to win held the men together. Before long the boats were loaded and set sail for New York. By early morning the fog deepened and hid them from view. At last they landed on the southern shores of Manhattan —New York City.

Nathan gave a prayer of thanks and fell on the cold ground to rest. He was completely exhausted.

Asher was with him in a moment. "Your head's as hot as a stove! You must go to bed, or it won't be a bullet that takes you!"

"There's more work to do," murmured Nathan. "We can't stay here long; the British will follow us. No doubt Washington will order us north of the city—perhaps to Harlem Heights."

He fell into a deep, feverish sleep.

A SPECIAL TASK

After a few days Nathan's fever broke, and he began to stir. Asher was beside him.

"Don't try to get up, Nathan. I'm speaking to you as an old friend, not as Captain Hale. You are still far from well."

"Thanks for taking care of me, old man. Don't worry. I'll be all right."

Just then a sergeant brought a message from Major Latimer asking Nathan to come to his headquarters.

"You can't go now!" protested Asher.

"But I must—these are orders," said Nathan. "Besides, it's my duty."

Slowly he got out of bed and fumbled with his clothing. Asher had cleaned his clothes. His fringed shirt was spotless, and his coat and breeches were brushed and fresh.

"How did you ever do it?" said Nathan. "I thought I'd never be able to wear these clothes after wallowing in that Brooklyn Heights mud."

"You should see most of the men," said Asher. "They look as if they'd been outfitted by an old clothes dealer! I never saw so many tattered hand-me-downs in my life! They don't even look like soldiers."

"How can I thank you enough," said Nathan, "for all you have done."

Asher laughed. "It's small pay for what you have done for me! But be careful. You really should stay in bed a few days longer to get your strength."

"I'll see what Major Latimer wants, and if he needs me I must go, Asher. Things are at a dangerous pass right now."

Nathan reported for duty. Major Latimer looked up from his papers. "Captain Hale, I am pleased to tell you that you have been chosen by General Washington to be in a special regiment of rangers under the command of Colonel Knowlton."

"I won't be with you and Colonel Webb any longer?" asked Nathan.

"Well, not for now, anyway. This regiment has been set aside for special work. You and the other men chosen are to try to get as close to enemy lines as possible.

Learn what they are doing and what they are planning. At this time none of you will be asked to go within the enemy lines, so you won't be considered spies. If you are caught you will be made prisoners of war."

"If those are General Washington's wishes, I'll do it," said Nathan.

Major Latimer continued, "Many of the men are discouraged. Some are going home. We need men with a sense of duty."

Nathan told his men that he had been ordered elsewhere and charged them to have faith in General Washington's plans.

Tom, Steve, and the others crowded around wishing Nathan well in his new work. But when he got back to his tent Asher said, "You're not well enough."

"I feel well enough, Asher. After all, I'm just one person. This country is made up of many people. I must do my part to give them the right to live the way they wish to live—with the spirit of freedom."

The tent flaps breezed open and Bill Hull pushed his tall body through. "Shades of Yale!" he said. "You sound like the old college debater. I'm inclined to take Asher's part. I don't think you're well enough to start on a new job."

"Let's put it this way," said Nathan calmly. "Orders are orders, and I have received mine. I have to carry them out, Bill."

"That ends the debate," Bill said, turning toward Asher. "I always did come out the loser with Nathan." He turned to Nathan. "By the way, I've heard that Gilbert Saltonstall plans to go into the Marines now that he can leave home."

"He'll do a wonderful job there," said Nathan. "Everybody has his own special job and I hope I can do mine."

Nathan was appointed to head one of the four companies in Colonel Knowlton's regiment of rangers.

They scouted near enemy lines and patrolled the shore but they learned nothing of importance.

One evening Nathan was asked to report to Colonel Knowlton. When he reached the Colonel's tent he found a group of men looking somewhat worried.

Nathan was asked to wait on a bench beside them. Presently Colonel Knowlton stood. "You are wondering why you have been called here." He looked earnestly at each man, then continued in a slow, even voice. "Men, you have been chosen from my regiment because you are the most outstanding soldiers I have. There is need now for *one* among you to do a very special task. I am not going to select that one. Whoever takes this duty will have to do it of his own free will."

The men shuffled and looked at each other.

What sort of task was this going to be? Nathan wondered.

Colonel Knowlton said, "General Washington has asked me to get one man who will be willing to go through enemy lines to gather information and make maps of British fortifications. This person must be able to draw plans well and write notes in code.

"It won't mean extra pay—and it won't mean a gain in rank. It will mean that the man who goes has real love for his country. The man who goes will have to go in plain clothes. If he is caught he will be treated as a spy. Now go to your tents and think this over. If there is one among you who is willing to take this risk, report to me in the morning."

Nathan's mind was busy. "I know how to make plans, and I could write notes in Latin. Should I go? If I get caught I'll never see my family again. And what about Alice? What shall I do? I have said I would do *anything* for my country."

He decided to confide in Bill Hull.

He told him what Colonel Knowlton had said. "Bill, I feel it is my duty to go. I could dress as a school-teacher."

"Not you, Nathan! The risk is too great. Besides, you have powder marks on your face from battle; you might be detected as a soldier."

"The marks are slight," said Nathan.

"Think what you might be giving up!" pleaded Bill. "You're only twenty-one!"

"I've thought of all that," said Nathan, "I've thought of my home and my family. But they would want me to do what I think is right."

Bill shook his head.

"I must go, Bill. I can do the things required, and besides I can run fast if the British chase me!"

"But this is asking too much of a man!" said Bill. "It's above the line of duty. It might even mean—"

Nathan broke in, "I know. It's above the line of duty but General Washington would not have asked it if it weren't vital."

"I know you'd be the best man to go, Nathan, but I wish it could be someone else."

"I must go," said Nathan. "It's my duty."

The two friends parted.

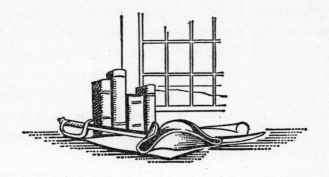

IN PATH OF DANGER

That night sleep would not come. Plans raced through Nathan's head.

How could he cross the British lines? English boats were patrolling the New York coast, so he must go to some Connecticut town to cross over to Long Island.

Norwalk! That was it. His old friend, Captain Pond, sailed from there at stated times, and Norwalk was almost opposite Huntington on Long Island!

With that decided, Nathan began to think about taking someone with him as far as Norwalk. Who would be the best one to take? Asher—his devoted friend? Asher would argue that Nathan was not well enough to go on such a trip.

Bill Hull? No. Bill would say he shouldn't go at all.

Stephen Hempstead—he was the one! Steve was always ready for adventure and he was level headed too. He was also a good walker and would not mind going on foot to Norwalk. Best of all, Steve could keep a secret.

Nathan fell into a deep sleep and awoke the next morning feeling refreshed. "You look more like your old self," said Asher. "But your cheeks are a little flushed. Don't have a fever, do you?"

"Oh, no," said Nathan. "I'm just excited. I'm going to be away for about two weeks. If our regiment moves while I'm gone be sure to take my things along. I'll join you again when I come back."

Nathan wanted to tell Asher that if he did not return at all to take his things home and tell his family that he loved them all very, very much. But that would reveal the danger of the journey. Nathan made an effort to put away all thoughts of his future plans until the war was over. He would keep his feeling for Alice locked in his heart until then.

That night when all was quiet he and Stephen Hempstead began their walk to Norwalk. Nathan, in a brown suit made of homespun wool and a big round hat, looked like the schoolmaster he had been before the war.

Steve eyed him critically. "Nathan, you don't look a bit like a spy!"

"Good," said Nathan, "I hope the British agree with you!"

For a while Nathan and Stephen did not talk as they trudged over a path near the shore. The path led over beautiful Connecticut woodlands. The trees with their early fall colors sparkled as the sun rose. Beyond the trees were the blue waters of the Sound. Boats could be seen plying their way here and there.

"You know," said Nathan when they had stopped to rest a moment, "it hardly seems possible that I was graduated from Yale only three years ago.

Steve said, "How long a person lives isn't important. It's how well he lives!"

"I think that too," said Nathan.

"I haven't spotted any British patrol ships for quite a while."

"Neither have I," said Steve.

"I don't think we'll have to wait very long for Captain Pond because he's about due here with the "Schuyler," said Nathan.

"I wish I could go with you," said Steve. He sounded sad.

"I wish so too," said Nathan, "but the order calls for one man, so that's the way it'll have to be. Steve, wait in Norwalk until you get news of me. I'll try to make it back here, but something might happen to change my plans. I'll have to find my way to General Washington's headquarters some way."

Nathan looked at the silver buckles on his shoes.

"These look too good for a poor schoolmaster out of a job. You take them and keep them for me."

He handed the buckles to Steve and took out his watch. He started to hand it to Steve too. But he thought a moment. "Steve, I think I'll keep this. Surely a poor schoolmaster could be permitted a watch!"

He looked long at the timepiece. Visions of home and family came to him. Then he looked out at the waves beating against the shore.

"Captain Pond's boat is coming in!"

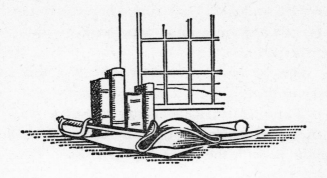

SECRET MISSION

It was night when Nathan landed in an out-of-the-way cove near Huntington. He was now in Tory territory among enemies. Nathan knew that some of them might not be strangers to him, for he had spent five months there helping build fortifications for the colonists. He well knew that many of the inhabitants shifted their loyalty according to which side seemed to be winning. Perhaps, among these people, he could find some who were willing to help him. But he must be careful for some of the people he had met before might recognize him now!

Ahead of him, on a little wooded lane, was an inn made of brown shingles or "shakes." Its comfortable appearance decided Nathan that it would be wise to stop for the night. He might hear news of the things that had happened since he left New York. He knew he must not act strangely or people would notice him. Steadily he approached the inn.

The fat innkeeper asked sullenly, "Are you a stranger in these parts?"

"I'm a Dutch schoolmaster out of a job," said Nathan. "The rebels are thick in Connecticut, and I wanted to be with the Tories. Do you know of any jobs on Long Island?"

"Don't know as I do," said the innkeeper.

"Well, I'll stay for the night," said Nathan quickly, "but I must be on my way tomorrow. How about supper?"

The innkeeper put some bread on the table and shuffled off.

While Nathan was waiting for him to get the rest of the meal, two strangers sat at a table near him. They were talking excitedly.

Nathan munched his bread but did not look up.

"Of all the blustering idiots!" said one. "Those rebels take the cake! They couldn't stand up to us on Long Island and now General Howe has chased them out of the lower part of New York City! They're back on Harlem Heights now."

"That's good!" said the other. "Soon, we'll have them chased out entirely. Colonel Knowlton was killed and so were other leaders."

Nathan was shocked. His own Colonel killed!

The news stung him. He tried not to seem interested but it was difficult to control himself.

Brave Colonel Knowlton killed, and his friends chased out of the lower part of the city! General Howe must have attacked shortly after he left. That meant that Asher and the rest of his company had moved. How many of his friends had been killed? What would be the British's next move? It was more important than ever that he discover their plans and get the information to General Washington quickly.

He scarcely noticed when the innkeeper put down a plate of stew. His thoughts were tumbling over one another. He must work his way through Long Island toward New York as fast as possible and get within the enemy lines. There would not be time to go back to Norwalk. He must get through the British lines in lower New York and reach the colonial stronghold in Harlem. Later he could send word to Steve in Norwalk. Now he must find the British strongholds, draw pictures of their positions, and learn their intentions!

Nathan kept his ears open for further comments from the strangers. He wondered who they were. They weren't soldiers because they were not in uniform. They were dressed like well-to-do merchants. They had powdered wigs, high ruffled collars, and coats with long tails that partly covered silken breeches. One wore a scarlet cape that fell from his shoulders to the floor.

Nathan, in his plain brown suit, didn't attract any attention.

"The rebellion ought to be over quickly," said one bewigged gentleman. "The British have so many more men than the rebels. My son is a Major, and he says the Continental soldiers are no match for us. I was at his camp opposite Hell Gate the other day."

Nathan almost jumped out of his chair. The British had a camp on Long Island opposite Hell Gate!

Hell Gate was a narrow place in the water. He would go there and see what he could find out!

As soon as the two Tories had gone Nathan went to his room.

By candlelight, he took a piece of very thin paper and wrote on it in Latin. He hid the paper under the innersole of his shoe.

The next day Nathan mingled with the people. Since the British had won the battle of Long Island and had chased the colonials out of lower New York, people seemed to feel that everything would be over soon.

Nathan listened closely to the people talking and learned that the American lines now extended from the mouth of the Harlem River, east and west, across Manhattan Island. He watched farmers loading their wagons with food for the British Army in New York City.

Boat loads of Tories were coming over from Connecticut to claim the King's protection.

Here and there Nathan spotted the red-coated soldiers. He tried to keep out of their way, but he watched their movements. Some citizens of Long Island who had not taken sides before now felt that it was time to join the British ranks.

Nathan passed among these people unnoticed. His round, broad-brimmed brown hat partly hid his face. He found where the British encampments were and at night he carefully drew maps on the thin paper and added them to the notes already secreted in his shoes.

After he had been on Long Island five days he heard two officers mention a night meeting to be held in a farmhouse taken over for headquarters.

When it was dusk and most people had gone indoors for supper Nathan found his way to the farmhouse. A lone sentinel was stationed near. By going around through the woods Nathan avoided his notice.

He found a place where he might hide that night to overhear any conversation.

In the main room of the farmhouse was a large table where the officers would likely sit during their meeting. Nathan peered at it through a small window hidden from the road by a lean-to. This would be the place to hide!

As he picked his way through the dooryard toward the woods where he planned to rest until nightfall, he came upon a large hole covered by loose boards.

"An open well! I'll have to look out for this!" he thought. Then he spotted an apple tree nearby and determined to avoid going near this spot in the dark. The apple tree would help him know where it was.

In the woods Nathan lay down to rest and then ate a simple meal of hardtack and fresh fruit. He must get out of here tonight! It had seemed to him that the fruit merchant had looked at him strangely. Perhaps it was imagination but he must leave as soon as possible.

In the distance he could hear the surf beating against the shores. He knew that many boats from time to time plied their way between Flushing and Manhattan. But they would be British boats now! Could there possibly be one among them owned by a patriot? What would he do after he heard what the officers had to say? Should he try to go all the way back to Huntington and cross to Norwalk and then over to Washington's headquarters on Harlem? That would take days.

Nathan wondered if Steve was still waiting for him at Norwalk. He knew that General Washington would want news immediately. He was anxious to give him the plans that he had so painstakingly made. Nathan determined that after the meeting tonight he must make his way to the port and wait for a boat that would take him to Manhattan. Perhaps he could find a friendly skipper. If not, he could still pass for an unfortunate schoolmaster as he had done these past days.

Slowly darkness fell, and the officers began to ride in and take their places at the table in the farmhouse. Nathan crawled through the grass until he reached the small window near the lean-to. Putting his ear close to the glass, he listened.

"There is little we can do," said one of the officers, "as long as Washington's army stands across the top of Manhattan Island. If we could get up the Hudson River to the rear of the American right, and at the same time land troops from the Sound in the rear of the American left, it might be possible to make Washington surrender. Then if we could take Fort Washington and Fort Lee—"

Nathan heard a movement in the grass behind him. A figure was approaching. Although Nathan could not see the features that swagger from side to side was unmistakable. Mark Thorne!

Nathan realized that the fruit merchant had recognized him and told Mark. He had been watched!

With a dash similar to the ones he had made in athletics at Yale, Nathan ran in the direction of the shore. Glancing quickly over his shoulder he could see Mark waving a dagger.

Nathan dared not look again. He might trip and fall. Jumping over a stone fence he tore along at great speed.

Suddenly, a shriek of terror filled the air. It was Mark! The open well!

"What's up?" shouted a voice from the darkness.

"It must be a spy!" shouted another.

"Who shrieked?" asked another.

Nathan did not stop running.

It seemed as if the woods and road were alive with people running.

Nearer and nearer Nathan came to the shore. If only there were more trees to hide behind!

He spied a sail on the water—a ship. Could it be a friendly one? He ran faster.

Without warning, a soldier appeared in front of him.

"Who goes there? Give the password!"

Nathan was hedged between soldiers behind him and in front.

"It looks mighty strange," said an officer, "to see a schoolmaster out running at night. Take him to General Howe for questioning! Colonel Rogers' boat will be sailing tonight."

Nathan knew that Rogers was Lieutenant-Colonel Robert Rogers, a famous ranger for the British. He had a reputation as a clever and brave man.

Nathan wondered if there would be any way of escaping from the boat?

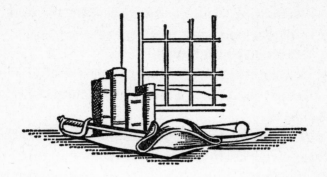

HIS REGRET

Nathan couldn't help admire Colonel Rogers. He was handsome and pleasant, and his strong features made him stand out.

"It's too bad he isn't on our side!" thought Nathan. "War divides men who otherwise might be friends."

Colonel Rogers did not have Nathan searched. "We will take this man directly to General Howe at Beekman House for questioning."

Nathan was led to a cabin where guards were posted to watch him. Through the porthole he could see the skyline of New York coming into view. It had a strange glare. Then someone shouted, "New York City's on fire! I bet the rebels are responsible for that!"

Nathan thought quickly. Would the fire make escape possible? Or would the British increase their guard immediately. The men on the boat were furious about the fire. Nathan was sorry too. He loved the city, and he knew the colonials would be blamed.

To avoid the fire Colonel Rogers landed up the river beyond the flames. This brought Nathan closer to colonial lines.

Two husky guards walked beside Nathan. He noticed that men were hurrying here and there trying to find their belongings while others were running with buckets of water.

He thought of his quiet home in Connecticut and hoped that it would always be quiet and peaceful and safe there. It would be if the colonial army could win independence.

But now, what faced them—and what faced him? The city was in flames, the Tories in a rage, and he was in a trap!

If only General Howe did not search him he might be able to talk himself out of the trouble! He might convince the General he was a schoolmaster. He must get those notes and maps in his shoes to General Washington. Then it wouldn't matter what happened to him!

He was led into a huge room where General Howe sat at a big carved desk. "Your name?" asked General Howe. He was stockily built, and Nathan felt the authority of his words.

"Nathan Hale."

"We have a man in our service by the name of Hale," said General Howe. "He is our Deputy Commissary of Prisoners."

Turning to a guard he said, "Bring Hale here!"

Nathan knew that it must be his cousin Samuel.

General Howe, motioned to one of the guards, "Search the prisoner!"

Nathan's heart sank. He had gladly risked his life to make those notes and now he might lose them.

The guard examined the seams and lining of his coat. He searched his pockets and the seams of his breeches. Finally he came to his shoes and discovered the papers.

"Ah! notes in some strange tongue."

"Latin!" exclaimed the General, patting his wig. "Our man Hale can read Latin, get him in here!"

Then Nathan was certain that this "Hale" would be his cousin Samuel.

What would Samuel do when he saw him?

Nathan realized that since the notes had been found there was nothing his cousin could say to change his fate. Even if Samuel lied about the notes there were the drawings! Nathan knew there was no hope.

At that moment Samuel was brought into the room. He did not say anything to Nathan.

"Do you know this prisoner?" asked General Howe.

Samuel hesitated. "Yes Sir, but I do not know why he is here."

Nathan spoke slowly, "I tried to help my country gain freedom."

General Howe looked at him with a cold eye. "Do you know the penalty for spying?"

"Yes," said Nathan.

"You are to be hanged in the morning," said General Howe.

Samuel left the room visibly shaken.

That night Nathan was put in the charge of the huge Provost Marshal Cunningham—a surly man.

"You'll sleep in the greenhouse tonight!" he snapped. "Then you can see the red glare from the city that your friends burned!"

Nathan felt sick at heart, but one thought remained with him. "What happens to me is of small consequence but what happens to the hundreds of people living in this country and who will live here in the future, is important."

Nathan thought of his family and friends—his kind, serious father; his stepmother, who had been as dear as a mother to him; Enoch, who had always been his chum; and Asher. Beautiful and sweet Alice! Now he was glad that he had never declared his love for her, but had always kept it locked in his heart. It might have left a scar between him and Enoch.

"I know Alice knows deep down in her heart how I have felt all along," he thought. "Love is a hard thing to hide."

A sense of peace came over Nathan. His sacrifices had not been in vain. "It is impossible to suppress freedom" he thought.

The glare of the city became a beacon of light for him, and he fell asleep unafraid.

The next morning the air smelt of charred wood from the smouldering city.

Cunningham threw the greenhouse door open. "Out of here, you bloody rebel!"

He tied Nathan's hands behind his back and shoved him into a cart drawn by a scrawny horse. Then he scrambled into the back of the cart weighing it down with his ponderous frame.

The cart rumbled over the rough pavement. Cunningham glowered and scowled at Nathan. But Nathan didn't notice. Instead he looked out at the bright greensward dotted with tents in Artillery Park where the cart was coming to a stop. The overhanging trees were cooling in the warm September sunshine.

"Don't you know you're about to die!" Cunningham snarled.

"Yes, I know," said Nathan quietly.

"I never saw anyone like you! Don't you have any regrets?"

Nathan did not answer, but his gaze was steady.

A tall blond soldier came out of one of the tents and approached Nathan.

"I'm Captain John Montressor," he said. "Would you like to come into my tent while you're waiting to be called?"

"You are very kind, Captain," said Nathan.

Cunningham grunted as he followed the two into the tent.

"Is there anything you would like to have at this time?" asked Montressor.

"Yes," said Nathan. "May I have a Bible? I want to read some passages we used to read at home."

"There isn't a Bible anywhere around here!" snapped Cunningham.

"Then I would like to have paper and a pen," said Nathan.

Grudgingly Cunningham went for the things. Presently he entered the tent and gave Nathan a quill pen, ink, and some paper.

Nathan calmly took the paper and began to write:

New York City

September 22, 1776

That was as far as he could get for a moment. "What shall I say?" he thought. "My dear family—how could a letter ever take the place of seeing them? And my friends—how wonderful they have been!"

Then he began to pour out his thoughts on paper.

He had finished writing two letters when Cunningham came in. Grabbing Nathan's letters the gruff officer shoved them into his pocket, crumpling them as he did so.

"Your friends don't deserve any letters!" he growled.

Captain Montressor cried out, "That was a mean thing to do, Cunningham. The lad is brave and true! Would that *we* had a whole army like him!"

He took the letters from Cunningham. "I shall deliver the letters for you."

"If you could take the letters to my brother Enoch," said Nathan, "it would please me very much."

"I will!" said Captain Montressor.

Slowly, but calmly, Nathan walked to the cart that had now been placed under a tree. A rope was hanging from one of the limbs. From the cart Nathan looked over the small crowd that had gathered. Some of the faces looked scornful. Many showed pity.

Thoughts began to race through Nathan's mind.

"Mark got what he deserved," he thought. "But Colonel Knowlton—what a loss to the Colonial Army!

There will be countless deaths and much more suffering before independence will be gained. But it will come!"

He remembered Cunningham's question: *"Don't you have any regrets?"*

He looked at the people without fear and spoke in an unwavering voice. "I only regret that I have but one life to lose for my country!"

BIBLIOGRAPHY

Brown, Marion Marsh. *Young Nathan*. Philadelphia: The Westminster Press, 1949.

Darrow, Jane. *Nathan Hale*. New York: The Century Company, 1932.

Faulkner, Harold U., and Kepner, Tyler. *America, Its History and People*. 3rd edition. New York: Harper & Bros., 1942.

Gordy, Wilbur Fisk. *A History of the United States*. New York: Charles Scribners Sons, 1912.

Hogeboom, Amy, and Ware, John. *One Life to Lose*. New York: Lothrop, Lee & Shepherd Company, 1942.

Mann, Martha. *Nathan Hale, Patriot*. New York: Dodd, Mead & Company, 1944.

Miller, John C. *Triumph of Freedom 1775-1783*. Boston: Little, Brown and Company, 1948.

Pennypacker, Morton. *The Two Spies—Nathan Hale and Robert Townsend*. Boston: Houghton Mifflin Company, 1930.

Seymour, George Dudley. *Documentary Life of Nathan Hale*. New Haven, Conn.: Privately printed, 1941.

This book was set up, printed, and bound by Parthenon Press in Nashville, Tennessee. It is set in twelve on sixteen point Baskerville type on 60 lb. Carfax Eggshell.